My favorite

MW00890716

Here is a picture of my favorite meal:

My favorites

Spot's favorite book is *Where's Spot?*

My favorite books:

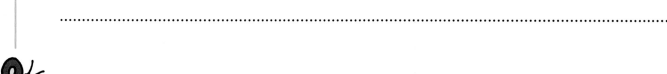

My favorites

Spot likes visiting the animals on the farm.

My favorite farm animal:

....

My other favorite animals:

....

Here is a drawing of the
animal I have/would like
to have as a pet:

At school

My school is called:

....

Spot's teacher is Miss Bear.

My teacher's name:

....

My teacher looks like this:

At school

Things I do at school: ....

....

....

....

....

....

Outings

On his walk Spot sees flowers and butterflies.

When I go for a walk, this is what I see:

....

At the park Spot says hello to the ducks.

When I go to the park, this is what I do:

....

....

....

Outings

Sometimes Spot goes to stay overnight at Steve's and he takes all his favorite things.

When I go to stay overnight, this is what I take:

Outings

I went on a picnic on (date) ....

with ....

The weather was ....

I ate ....

We played ....

Holidays

My favorite holiday: ....

I spent the day with ....

I ate ....

My presents: ....

....

My birthday

Date: ....

At my birthday party we ate:

....

There were .... candles on my cake.

We played ....

My presents: ....

....

....

....

A friend's birthday party

Friend's name: ....

Age: ....

The cake looked like this:

Here is the invitation:

Vacation

Sam and Sally took Spot to the beach.

My vacation was at

....

Date: ....

This drawing shows how we got there:

Vacation

Here are some things
I collected:

Photographs & souvenirs

Photographs & souvenirs

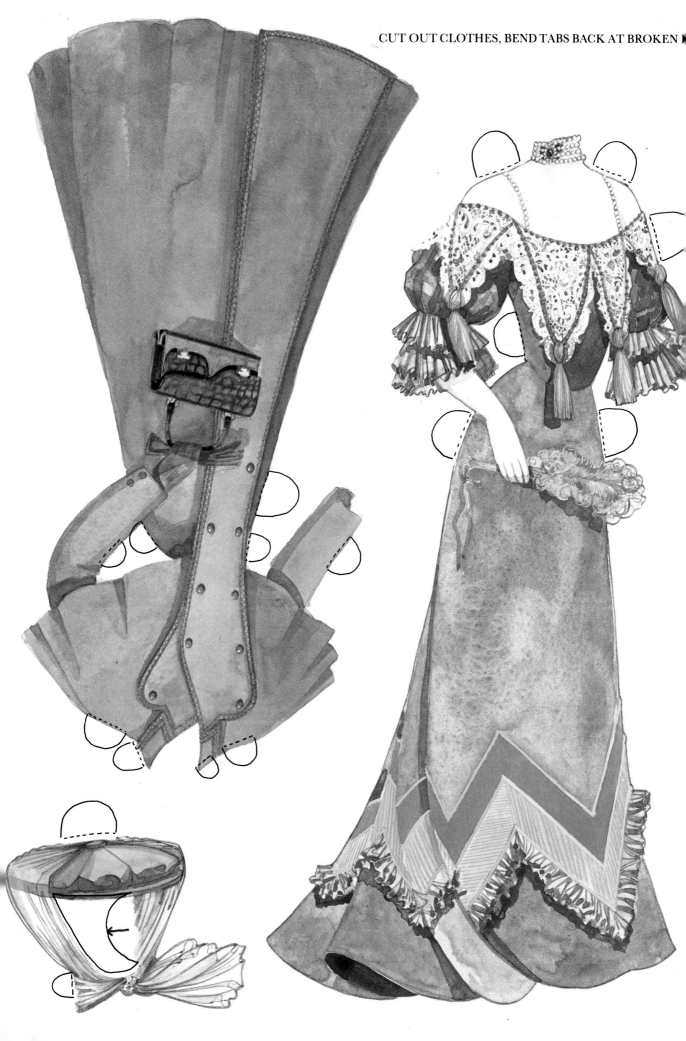

TAILOR MADE
FACE CLOTH
MOTOR COAT
DOUBLE-BREASTED
WITH CAPE EFFECT
LINED TO THE
WAIST WITH
SILK

CROCODILE
VANITY
BAG

OSTRICH FEATHER
FAN

SILK EVENING
GOWN.
TRIMMED WITH
LACE
SILK TASSELS
VELVET RIBBON
AND PEARLS

LADIES'
FACE CLOTH
MOTOR
CAP

CUT SLITS IN HATS AT BLACK LINE.

MANTLE.
PEAU DE
SOIE
TRIMMED
WITH
PASSEMENTERIE
AND FRILLS OF
KILTED
CHIFFON

TEA JACKET.
SILK
MERVEILLEUX
TUCKED AND
TRIMMED
WITH
BEIGE LACE

STRAW HAT
DECORATED
WITH OSTRICH FEATHERS
AND FLOWERS

STRAW HAT
DECORATED
WITH
FEATHERS

CREAM
FLANNEL
BOLERO

STRAW
BOATER

CREAM
FLANNEL
SKIRT

CUT OUT CLOTHES, BEND TABS BACK AT BROKEN LINE

CUT SLITS IN HATS AT BLACK LINE.

BLUE SERGE
HAT

STRAW BOATER
GREEN RIBBON
AND FLOWERS

BLUE
SERGE
COAT.
COLLAR
AND CUFFS
TRIMMED
WITH
INSERTION
AND
FEATHER
STITCHING

WHITE
LAWN
PINAFORE
TRIMMED
WITH
LACE

LACE
SUN
BONNET

STRAW
HAT
DECORATED
WITH
RIBBONS

DRESS
IN
WHITE
ZEPHYR
EMBROIDERED
IN
WHITE

GYM
SLIP

SERGE
COAT
TRIMMED
WITH
SILK
BRAID

THE EDWARDIANS

Background to the Period

The Edwardian Era, named after Edward VII, son of Queen Victoria, describes the years between 1900 and the outbreak of the First World War in 1914. Edward came to the throne in 1901 and died 1910.

Victoria's reign had been long and stable, marked by a growth in the country's prosperity, and its influence all over the world through its thriving colonies and trade.

Victoria was a widow for a great part of her reign, sadly mourning her beloved husband, Albert. Her life as a Christian and dutiful monarch, loving wife and mother, set the pattern for Victorian society.

This was the backgound to Edward's accession to the throne. He had already established a life-style marked by a love of extravagance and pleasure. Although married to the beautiful Queen Alexandra, he had many mistresses and made no secret of his enjoyment of the company of beautiful women. The King loved yachting, horse racing and the theatre. He greatly admired the French for their style and fashion. He enjoyed the company of a wide range of witty and amusing people including many of the country's new rich industrialists, whose money often financed the continual round of sporting and social events which marked the King's short reign.

EDWARD VII

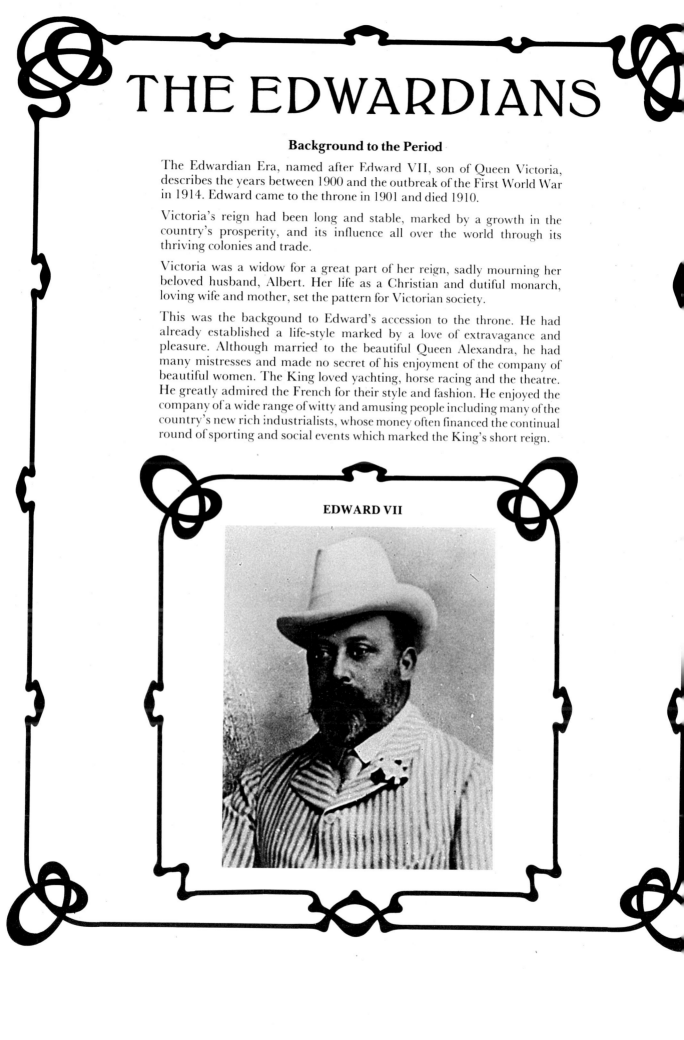

ouses, furniture, household objects and clothes of any
riod reflect very clearly their time. In Edwardian days, the
owth of factories making goods in quantity meant that
xtiles, pottery, building materials and domestic utensils
re more widely available to many more people.

Remington Standard
Typewriter.
The New Model No. 7.

The Portable
Telephone.

lthough accepting the undoubted benefits that the
manufacturing process could bring, even in the 1860's some
rtists felt that there would inevitably be a fall in the
andard of design. These artists were known as The Arts
nd Crafts Movement. They wanted to design for the future,
ut felt it was important to study nature and to use the skills
f good craftsmen working in fine (often local) materials, to
arry out their designs.

n the early twentieth century, architects and designers
fluenced by The Arts and Crafts Movement were: Charles
ennie Mackintosh, Edwin Lutyens and C.F.A. Voysey.
hey were responsible for a profound change in the
ppearance of housing and furniture in the following
ecades.

t this time, there were also enormous advances in science
nd engineering, the effects of which were beginning to be felt
n the home. Some households now boasted electric lighting,
telephone, and even a motor car.

he use of photography was becoming widespread.
ndividuals and families were recorded, posed in their best
lothes in the photographer's studio. More informal
hotographs survive from this time, taken by enthusiastic
mateurs.

The Clothes of the Period

Although the Edwardian age seems carefree when compared
with Victorian times, manners and customs at that time were
still rather rigid. The children of wealthier families were
looked after by a nanny who supervised their meals in a
separate part of the house, set aside as nursery and
schoolroom. Mama and Papa would visit the children in the
nursery, or arrange with Nanny to have the children brought
down dressed properly with hair well brushed and
fingernails scrubbed. Older children would go to private day
school or boarding school rather than the "Board" schools
which were run by the local councils.

For both adults and children there was felt to be a correct
attire for each occasion. This was usually a complete outfit
down to the last detail only to be worn for that particular part
of the day or for that particular sporting or leisure activity.

Children's Clothes

Small children wore clothes that allowed fairly unrestricted
movement. Little boys up to the age of four or five would
wear dresses similar to their sisters, these dresses were of the
finest white cotton and lace, beautifully embroidered by
hand; spotless and perfectly starched and ironed!

Photographs of the royal princes, Edward and George, in
their sailor suits set a fashion for children of all ages, both
boys and girls.

After the age of five, boys wore small versions of the Norfolk
jacket or Eton suit - both of these were worn with
knickerbockers and thick knee-high socks. Older boys wore
the Eton suit with long trousers. Little girls wore stiffly
starched white cotton lawn or cotton piqué dresses,
decorated with fine embroidery, with a contrasting sash and
black shoes and stockings.

CUT ALONG BLACK LINE.

All children would be expected to wear hats or bonnets when out of doors - even for play.

Both boys and girls were beginning to wear more practical clothes in school. Rugger and football clothes for boys were white knee length shorts, knee-high socks and open-necked shirts. Girls receiving private education would possibly have worn the newly introduced gym slip.

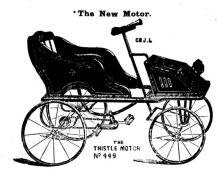

*The New Motor.

THE THISTLE MOTOR Nº 449

Ladies' Clothes

Edwardian women were required to be objects of admiration. The day clothes reflected the sunny optimism of the age with pastel shades and floral embroidery.

The basic shape of the "ideal" female had changed as a result of the so-called "health corset". This was designed to give the woman a tiny waist and a flat stomach. In so doing, it tilted the bust forward and the hips back giving the side view a distinct 'S' shape.

Dresses were hand-made and exquisite, often fashioned from fine silks such as chiffon, crêpe de Chine or tulle. They were decorated with clusters of ribbon, embroidery, handpainted decorations and intricate lace. For day wear, the body was completely covered from the high collar stiffened with bone to the tapering wrist-hugging sleeves. Out of doors each dress would have been worn with a particular hat. The hat would be large and generously decorated with feathers and flowers, and worn tilted forward to offset the weight of the dress behind.

The evening dress was usually dramatically low-cut, possibly black and covered with sequins. Alternatively, they were made in pastel shades, the decoration even more exquiste than that used for the day dresses, including tassels and clusters of pearls, lace appliqué, a beautiful corsage and a feather boa. Paris was the inspiration for these dresses. Couturiers designed each handmade creation for a particular client. No couturier of repute would have dreamt of copying another.

The English contribution to the clothing of women at this time was the 'tailor made'. Middle class young women were beginning to earn their own livings and they wore beautifully tailored skirts and jackets to go about their occupations as governesses or typists. Wealthier women adopted the fashion when in the country, or for travelling.

CORSETS, LINGERIE FINE

A LA SAMARITAINE

Women also had costumes designed for particular sports. This was another trend that influenced the way in which clothes were soon to become more practical. There were shorter skirts for roller-skating, bloomers for cycling and more generously cut sleeves for tennis.

FOLD FLAP UP AT BROKEN LINE.

When you have finished changing the clothes, put them flat inside these pages and place inside the wardrobe at the end of the book.

Gentlemen's Clothes

Strict rules applied to the correct dress for men. The frock coat with top hat was considered proper formal wear, with the tailcoat and top hat for the evening. Suits with trousers, jacket and waistcoat made of the same material were becoming more popular. Overcoats for formal wear had to be elegant and fitting. For travelling and motoring long full coats were correct.

Every sport had its particular attire. The Norfolk jacket had been popularised by the then Prince of Wales who wore it for shooting in Norfolk. Straw boaters and striped blazers were worn with cream flannel trousers for gentle river sports, while the reefer jacket and peaked cap would have been worn for yachting. Motoring required a large wardrobe of special protective garments.

Correct accessories were of great importance: hats, canes, cufflinks, tie pins, gloves; equally important was when and how to wear them.

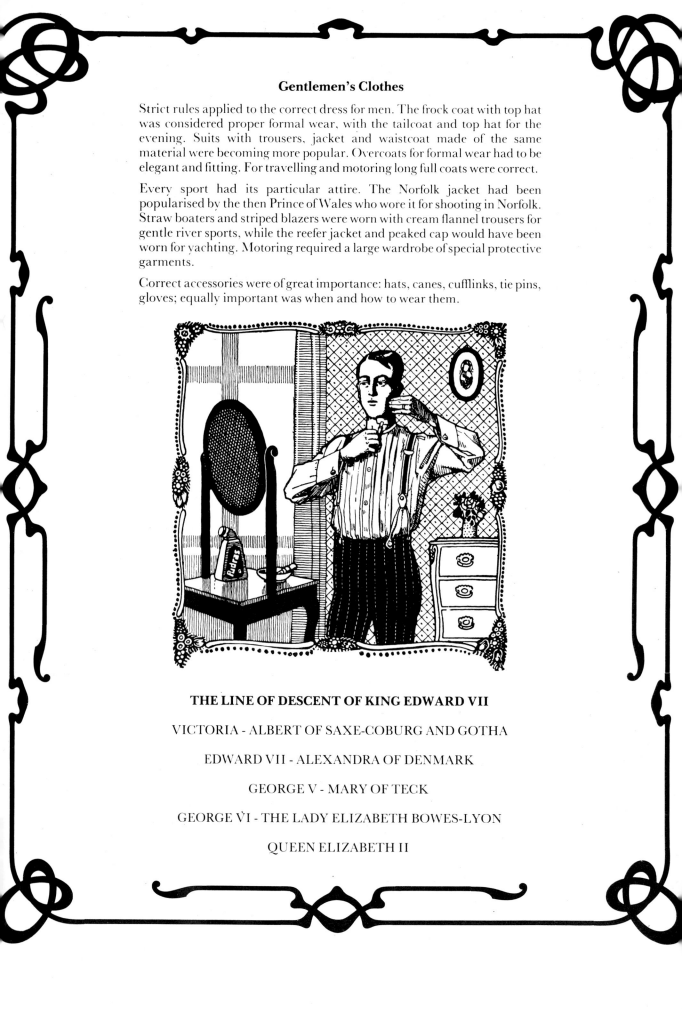

THE LINE OF DESCENT OF KING EDWARD VII

VICTORIA - ALBERT OF SAXE-COBURG AND GOTHA

EDWARD VII - ALEXANDRA OF DENMARK

GEORGE V - MARY OF TECK

GEORGE VI - THE LADY ELIZABETH BOWES-LYON

QUEEN ELIZABETH II

GREY
HAIRLINE
STRIPED
ETON SUIT
TROUSERS

VICUNA
ETON JACKET
AND
WAISTCOAT

BOY'S
SILK
TOP
HAT

SCOTCH
TWEED
CAP

BOY'S
FROCK.
JAPANESE
SILK WITH
FEATHER
STITCHING
AND
HEM-
STITCHING

SAILOR
HAT

SAILOR
HAT

NORFOLK
SUIT.
SCOTCH
TWEED

BLUE
TWILL
SERGE
CLYDE
SUIT

GABARDINE
SAILOR
TOP

MOTOR CAP
WITH BACK FALL
AND LEATHER
LINING

MOTOR COAT.
DOUBLE BREASTED
ALL WOOL TWEED
RAIN PROOF WITH
DETACHABLE
LEATHER
LINING

REEFER
JACKET.
DOUBLE BREASTED
BLUE SERGE

YACHTING CAP.
LEATHER PEAK

PANAMA
GRASS
HOMBURG

DINING JACKET
BEST ELASTIC TWILL
LINED IN SILK WITH
SILK ROLL COLLAR

INVERNESS CAPE
BLACK VICUNA CLOTH
LINED THROUGHOUT
WITH
ITALIAN
SATIN

TOP HAT.
GENTLEMAN'S
SILK